OVER IN THE RAIN FOREST

For Oscar of Belize and Mario of Panama —
two "natural" teachers who shared their knowledge
of and passion for the rain forest with us.
—C.R. & P.R.

For Maryam
—C.S.

ISBN 0-439-40980-2

Text copyright © 2003 by Connie and Peter Roop.
Illustrations copyright © 2003 by Carol Schwartz.
All rights reserved. Published by Scholastic Inc.
SCHOLASTIC and associated logos are trademarks and/or registered trademarks of Scholastic Inc.

12 11 10 9 8 7 6 5 4 3 2   3 4 5 6 7 8/0

Printed in the U.S.A.
First printing, March 2003

OVER IN THE RAIN FOREST

by Connie and Peter Roop

Illustrated by Carol Schwartz

SCHOLASTIC INC.
New York   Toronto   London   Auckland   Sydney
Mexico City   New Delhi   Hong Kong   Buenos Aires

Introduction

Over in the Rain Forest uses the traditional rhythms and rhymes of the folk song "Over in the Meadow." Tropical rain forests are found around and near the earth's equator. Year-round, the rain forest is hot and humid. Half of all animals and plants live in the rain forest. Howler monkeys and kinkajous are found in the canopy. Harpy eagles land on the tallest rain forest treetops. Leafcutter ants and peccaries live on the forest floor. You can *count* on animal fun as you journey over in the rain forest.

Over in the rain forest
under the hot, tropical sun

Lived a three-toed sloth
And her little sloth one.

"Climb," said the mother.
"I climb," said the one.
So they climbed all day under the hot, tropical sun.

Over in the rain forest where the kapok trees grew
Lived a brightly colored toucan
And her little chicks two.

"Fly," said the mother.
"We fly," said the two.
So they flew all day where the kapok trees grew.

Over in the rain forest under a canopy of trees
Lived a howler monkey mother
And her little monkeys three.

"Howl," said the mother.
"We howl," said the three.
So they howled all day under a canopy of trees.

Over in the rain forest on the forest floor
Lived a hungry peccary
And her little peccaries four.

"Root," said the mother.
"We root," said the four.
So they rooted all day on the forest floor.

Over in the rain forest where the harpy eagles dive
Lived a poison dart frog
And her little frogs five.

"Hop," said the mother.
"We hop," said the five.
So they hopped all day where the harpy eagles dive.

Over in the rain forest in the wet leaves and sticks
Lived a leafcutter ant
And her little ants six.

"Cut," said the mother.
"We cut," said the six.
So they cut all day in the wet leaves and sticks.

Over in the rain forest where the river flows so even
Lived a sharp-toothed piranha
And her little piranhas seven.

"Snap," said the mother.
"We snap," said the seven.
So they snapped all day where the river flows so even.

Over in the rain forest when it was so late
Out came a kinkajou
And her little babies eight.

"Hunt," said the mother.
"We hunt," said the eight.
So they hunted for food when it was so late.

Over in the rain forest where the spotted jaguars climb
Flew a Blue Morpho butterfly
And her little babies nine.

"Flutter," said the mother.
"We flutter," said the nine.
So they fluttered all day where the spotted jaguars climb.

Over in the rain forest near the termites' den
Lived a long mother boa
And her little boas ten.

"Hide," said the mother.
"We hide," said the ten.
So they hid all day near the termites' den.

RAIN FOREST ANIMALS

Blue Morpho butterflies: These beautiful butterflies flash their bright blue wings when they fly. Resting on a tree, Blue Morpho butterflies fold their wings and become hard to see. This is because the undersides of their wings are dull brown.

boa snakes (Emerald): These snakes hang in the trees waiting for a meal to hop, walk, or crawl by. They like to eat birds and bats. They kill them by squeezing them with their coiled bodies.

harpy eagles: These sharp-eyed birds sit quietly in the tallest rain forest trees looking for tasty treats to eat. With their powerful feet, harpy eagles catch and eat sloths and monkeys.

howler monkeys: The loud roar of the howler monkey can be heard for miles. They travel in the trees in small groups called troops. Howler monkeys spend most of their time eating leaves and fruit or resting.

jaguars: These large cats hunt for animals in the forest. Jaguars eat peccaries, deer, turtles, and fish. Jaguars often stretch out and rest in the sun on a tree branch over water.

kinkajous: Ants and figs are the favorite foods of these night-time feeders. Kinkajous are relatives of raccoons. They have big eyes. Their tails help them balance and hold onto branches. Kinkajous can quickly jump from tree to tree.

leafcutter ants: These ants cut and carry leaves, flowers, and stems back to their nests. They chew the plants to help fungus grow. Then they eat the fungus!

peccaries: Peccaries are large, fat animals with sharp teeth. Peccaries use their piglike snouts to find seeds, nuts, and fruits on the forest floor.

piranhas: Watch out! These flat, wide-bodied fish will snap at you and the worm on your fish hook! Their top and bottom jaws have small, sharp teeth. They eat small fish and frogs, and small seeds and fruit which fall into the water.

poison dart frogs: By being brightly colored, these small, colorful creatures warn enemies that they are poisonous. Flashing red, yellow, green, or blue says, "Don't eat me, I'm poisonous!" Their sticky toe pads help them cling to smooth, wet leaves and branches. They can even hang upside down!

termites: These insects are experts at building nests. They make their nests in trees out of wood which they chew. Termites make covered trails to their nests so it is harder for birds and other animals to eat them.

three-toed sloths: These long-armed animals often hang upside down on tree branches by holding on with their hooklike claws. Sloths spend most of their time eating leaves. Sloths move very slowly, which makes them hard to see.

toucans: These colorful birds use their long bills to reach berries and fruit. To play, toucans toss fruit back and forth to each other. Toucans build their nests in holes in trees.

RAIN FOREST WORDS

canopy: Most trees in the rain forest grow up to the canopy layer—65-100 feet above the forest floor. The canopy tree leaves form a complete cover like a green carpet. In the canopy, it is hot during the day and cool at night. Most of the living things in a rain forest live in the canopy.

hot, tropical sun: The rain forests around the equator receive 12 hours of sunlight yearlong. The sunlight hits the earth's surface directly. This means the temperature is usually between 70°-85°F every day of the year.

kapok tree: These trees have bright red seed pods filled with a fuzzy fiber. Kapok trees grow to be some of the tallest and biggest trees in the rain forest.